W9-BVK-838

The Mouse's Wedding

A fable retold by RUTH BELOV GROSS

Pictures by SUSAN SWAN

SCHOLASTIC INC.

New York Toronto London Auckland Sydney

*Based on a 12th-century retelling by Marie de France from
"The Mouse Who Sought a Wife."*

ISBN 0-590-41870-X

12 11 10 9 8 7 6 5 4 3 2 1   8 9/8 0 1 2/9

Printed in the U.S.A.   08

For Edith and Henry

There was once a mouse who wanted a wife.
But he did not want just *any* wife.

"If I cannot have the daughter
of the most powerful thing in the world," he said,
"I do not want a wife at all."

So the mouse set off
to find the most powerful thing in the world.

He went to the sun.
"After all," the mouse thought, "what could be
more powerful than the sun?"

When the mouse came to the sun, he said,
"You are the most powerful thing in the world.
That is why I want to marry your daughter.
If I cannot have your daughter,
I do not want a wife at all."

"I am not the most powerful thing in the world,"
the sun said. "There is something stronger than I —
the cloud."

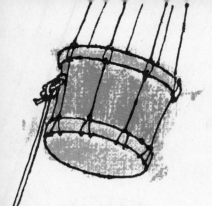

"The cloud!" said the mouse.

"Yes," said the sun.
"When the cloud comes in front of me,
I cannot shine on the earth."

"Then I will go to the cloud," said the mouse.
"You can keep your daughter!"

And the mouse set off to find the cloud.

When the mouse came to the cloud, he said,
"You are the most powerful thing in the world.
That is why I want to marry your daughter.
If I cannot have your daughter,
I do not want a wife at all."

"I am not the most powerful thing in the world,"
the cloud said. "There is something stronger than I —
the wind."

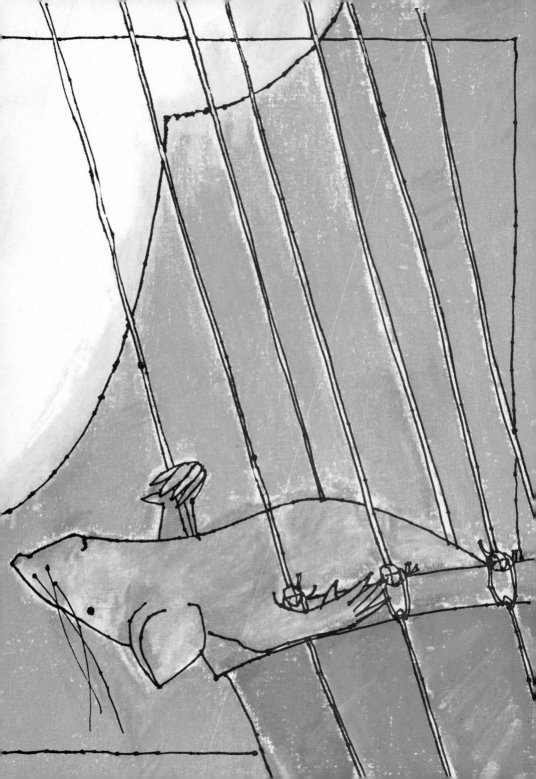

"The wind!" said the mouse.

"Yes," said the cloud.
"A puff of wind can blow me away."

"Then I will go to the wind," said the mouse.
"You can keep your daughter!"

And the mouse set off to find the wind.

When the mouse came to the wind, he said,
"You are the most powerful thing in the world.
That is why I want to marry your daughter.
If I cannot have your daughter,
I do not want a wife at all."

"I am not the most powerful thing in the world,"
the wind said.
"There is something stronger than I —
the tower that you see over there."

"The tower!" said the mouse.

"Yes," said the wind.
"I am not strong enough to blow it down."

"Then I will go to the tower," said the mouse.
"You can keep your daughter!"

And the mouse set off to find the tower.

When the mouse came to the tower, he said,
"I have looked everywhere
for the most powerful thing in the world.
I have been to the sun.
I have been to the cloud.
I have been to the wind.
And now I have come to you.

Are you the most powerful thing in the world?
If you are, I want to marry your daughter."

"I am not the most powerful thing in the world,"
the tower said. "There is something stronger than I —
a little mouse."

"A little mouse!" said the mouse.

"Yes," said the tower.

"Do you see the little mouse under my feet?
He is digging a hole there.
One day the hole will be so big
that I will topple right over.
The little mouse is much stronger than I.
He is the most powerful thing in the world."

"The most powerful thing in the world?"
said the mouse.
"Then I will go to the little mouse.
I will marry his daughter.
And we will have the finest wedding
in the world."

And they did.